Chapter 1 Test

Name _____

Write the letter of the correct answer.

_____ 1. All the nonliving things surrounding an organism are called ____.

    A. the environment   B. adaptations   C. an ecosystem

_____ 2. Plants need ____ to make food.

    A. light   B. protection   C. to stay warm

_____ 3. All living things are called ____.

    A. prey   B. organisms   C. partnerships

_____ 4. A change in a characteristic of a living thing that allows it to survive in its environment is called ____.

    A. an adaptation   B. an ecosystem   C. migration

_____ 5. Anything that can meet a need of a living thing is ____.

    A. an adaptation   B. competition   C. a resource

_____ 6. Some animals ____ from one ecosystem to another to find food and water.

    A. migrate   B. adapt   C. hibernate

_____ 7. During the coldest months of the year, some animals ____.

    A. compete   B. camouflage   C. hibernate

_____ 8. The living and nonliving things in an area are called ____.

    A. the environment   B. an ecosystem   C. a pod

_____ 9. Anything that makes the air, water, or land dirty is called ____.

    A. migration   B. pollution   C. adaptation

_____ 10. The changes that living things make in their ecosystems can be ____.

    A. adaptations   B. skills or behaviors   C. helpful and harmful

Label each statement as either *True* or *False*.

_____ 11. Competition occurs when living things use <u>different</u> resources.

_____ 12. Some living things work together in <u>partnerships</u>.

_____ 13. Some animals migrate as the <u>seasons</u> change.

_____ 14. Animals that blend in with their environment are protected by <u>mimicry</u>.

_____ 15. Living in <u>a group</u> makes it easier for animals to find food, to be better protected, and to care for their young.

Complete each statement. One word will not be used.

| behavior | prey | scientist |
| mimicry | protection | steward |

_____ 16. A Christian's role in his environment is to be a good ____ by taking care of what God has given him.

_____ 17. An adaptation may be a physical characteristic, a skill, or a ____.

_____ 18. All living things have basic needs such as food, water, and ____.

_____ 19. Some living things are protected by looking like other living things. This is called ____.

_____ 20. Animals that are food for other animals are called ____.

Write L if the item is a living thing and N if the item is a nonliving thing.

_____21. rain

_____22. sunflowers

_____23. weeds

_____24. pebbles

_____25. temperature

_____26. apple tree

Complete the section.

27. How can building new things affect the plants and animals in an ecosystem?

    _____

    _____

28. Name two defenses animals use for protection.

    _____

    _____

Chapter 2 Test

Name _____

Write the letter of the correct answer.

_____ 1. The knowledge or skill that an animal is born with is called ____.

     A. an instinct   B. hibernation   C. migration

_____ 2. Insects and spiders are two examples of ____.

     A. vertebrates   B. arthropods   C. reptiles

_____ 3. An insect becomes an adult through the process of ____.

     A. instincts   B. migration   C. metamorphosis

_____ 4. Some insects, such as ants, live together in a group called ____.

     A. a section   B. a colony   C. a society

_____ 5. A vertebrate has ____, but an invertebrate does not.

     A. a backbone   B. an exoskeleton   C. a probiscus

_____ 6. One characteristic of a spider is that it has ____.

     A. antennae   B. wings   C. no wings

Complete each statement. Some words will not be used.

abdomen	head	pedipalps	spiders
exoskeleton	insects	probiscus	spinnerets

_____ 7. The tube a butterfly uses to suck is a ____.

_____ 8. The hard outer covering of an arthropod is its ____.

_____ 9. The largest group of arthropods is ____.

_____ 10. To hold and poison the animals that spiders eat, they use ____ on their heads.

_____ 11. The silk used to build a web comes out through the ____ on a spider's abdomen.

_____ 12. In an insect, digestion occurs in the ____.

Label each statement as either *True* or *False*.

_____ 13. Arthropods have <u>jointed</u> legs.

_____ 14. An arthropod <u>stretches</u> its exoskeleton when the exoskeleton becomes too small.

_____ 15. Hunting and <u>trapping</u> are two ways spiders may get food.

_____ 16. A spider's web is made of <u>hair</u>.

_____ 17. Black widow and <u>brown recluse</u> spiders are poisonous.

Label the diagrams.

Parts of an Insect

18. _____

19. _____

20. _____

| abdomen |
| adult |
| egg |
| head |
| thorax |
| larva |
| pupa |

Complete Metamorphosis

21. _____

22. _____

23. _____

24. _____

Complete the chart comparing insects and spiders.

	Insects	Spiders
25.	Have _____ pairs of legs	Have 4 pairs of legs
26.	Have 3 body sections	Have _____ body sections

Complete the section.

27. Name two types of protection that insects have.

   _____

   _____

28. Why should people care for and protect insects such as bees?

   _____

   _____

   _____

   _____

Chapter 3 Test

Name _____

Write the letter of the correct answer.

_____ 1. All living things ____.

    A. reproduce   B. germinate   C. pollinate

_____ 2. The transfer of pollen from the stamen to the pistil is called ____.

    A. germination   B. pollination   C. dispersion

_____ 3. A scientist who studies plants is called ____.

    A. a botanist   B. an astronomer   C. a gardener

_____ 4. One classification of plants is ____.

    A. seeds or no tubes   B. cones or tubes   C. flowers or cones

_____ 5. New plants are always ____ the parent plants.

    A. different from   B. similar to   C. bigger than

_____ 6. Grouping things that have similar characteristics is called ____.

    A. classifying   B. dividing   C. sorting

_____ 7. Plants that produce their seeds in cones are called ____.

    A. conifers   B. deciduous   C. seedlings

Label each statement as either _True_ or _False_.

_____ 8. The <u>pistil</u> in a flower makes the seeds.

_____ 9. Plants can be pollinated by self-pollination, by <u>animals</u>, and by wind.

_____ 10. A young plant without flowers is called a <u>weed</u>.

_____ 11. A <u>fruit</u> is the part of a flowering plant that contains the seeds.

_____ 12. Seeds can be <u>dispersed</u> by animals or people, water, and wind.

Label the diagrams.

developing plant   seed coat
petal   stamen
pistil   stored food

Parts of a Flower

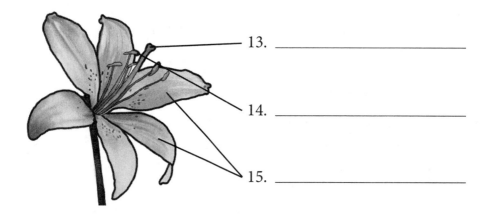

13. _____

14. _____

15. _____

Parts of a Seed

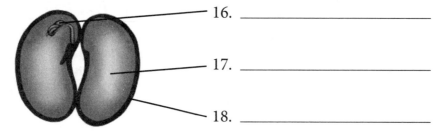

16. _____

17. _____

18. _____

Number the steps in a flowering plant's life cycle in order.
The first step is numbered for you.

___1___   A seed germinates.

_____19. A seedling grows.

_____20. The seeds disperse.

_____21. Flowers grow, and the plant becomes an adult.

_____22. The plant produces fruit.

_____23. An insect pollinates the plant.

Complete the section.

24. Identify two ways that people who handle plants can please the Lord in their work.

     _____

     _____

     _____

25. What are two of the conditions most seeds need to germinate?

     _____

     _____

26. A bee buzzes around you as you work in your family's garden. You observe the bee as it buzzes around a flower. You know that God designed some animals and flowers to work in partnership.

     Explain how the bee is helping the flower.

_____

_____

_____

Chapter 4 Test

Name _____

Match each definition with the correct term.

_____ 1. the weight of the object being moved

_____ 2. an object that makes work easier

_____ 3. the force that pulls objects toward the earth

_____ 4. the force applied to cause a simple machine to do work

_____ 5. the force that resists the movement of objects against each other

_____ 6. a change in position

> A. effort
> B. friction
> C. gravity
> D. load
> E. machine
> F. motion

Write the letter of the correct answer.

_____ 7. An object that makes work easier is called a ____.

    A. machine   B. fulcrum   C. load

_____ 8. A greater mass requires ____ force to move it.

    A. less   B. the same   C. a greater

_____ 9. A force moving an object over a distance is called ____.

    A. work   B. gravity   C. friction

_____ 10. The amount of work you do depends on how much ____ you use to move an object.

    A. gravity   B. energy   C. force

_____ 11. A block and tackle allows you to use ____ force when lifting an object because the rope moves a greater distance.

    A. less   B. the same   C. more

_____ 12. A wedge is one or more ____ used to force materials apart.

    A. levers   B. inclined planes   C. screws

_____ 13. A pulley is a ____ with a groove that can hold a rope.

    A. screw   B. wheel   C. axle

_____14. A lever is ____ that turns on a point.

        A. a thread   B. an axle   C. a bar

_____15. The inclined plane on a screw is called ____.

        A. the axle   B. the thread   C. a wedge

Label each statement as either _True_ or _False_.

_____16. A <u>force</u> is a push or a pull.

_____17. A screw is a <u>wedge</u> wound around an axle.

_____18. A <u>fulcrum</u> is the point on which a lever turns.

_____19. An inclined plane is a <u>hilly</u>, sloped surface.

_____20. The amount of effort needed on a lever is determined by the <u>gravity</u> between the effort and the fulcrum.

Label the type of simple machine.

inclined plane	screw
lever	wedge
pulley	wheel and axle

21. _____

22. _____

23. _____

24. _____

25. _____

26. _____

Complete the section.

27. Why should Christians value work and machines? _____

_____

_____

_____

28. Craig is playing catch with Patrick in the backyard. Patrick throws the ball past Craig into the grass. The ball drops to the ground and rolls to a stop in the short grass. What two forces caused the ball to drop to the ground and roll to a stop?

_____

_____

Chapter 5 Test

Name _____

Write the letter of the correct answer.

_____ 1. An unbroken path through which negative charges can flow is called a _____.

    A. circuit   B. series   C. conductor

_____ 2. When electrical charges build up on the surface of an object, _____ occurs.

    A. a series circuit   B. static electricity   C. current electricity

_____ 3. An object that attracts certain metals is called _____.

    A. a circuit   B. a magnet   C. an insulator

_____ 4. A material that does not allow electricity to flow through it easily is called _____.

    A. an insulator   B. a circuit   C. a conductor

_____ 5. A material that allows electricity to flow through it easily is called _____.

    A. a circuit   B. an insulator   C. a conductor

_____ 6. A magnetic field is caused when _____ flows through a circuit.

    A. air   B. a current   C. protons

_____ 7. A form of energy that involves the flow of electrical charges is called _____.

    A. a circuit   B. magnetism   C. electricity

_____ 8. Two things that use electromagnets are microwave ovens and _____.

    A. maglev trains   B. screwdrivers   C. paper currency

Count the number of positive and negative charges.
Write the number of each in the blanks next to each picture.
Decide whether the picture has a *negative* charge, has a *positive* charge,
or is *neutral*. Write the answer in the blank below.

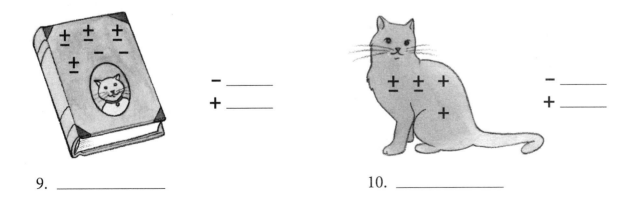

9. _____   10. _____

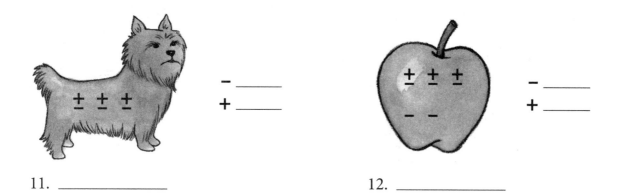

11. _____

12. _____

Complete each statement. One term will not be used.

> attract   magnetic field   neutral
> electromagnet   magnetism   poles
> generator   negative   repel

_____ 13. Objects with the same kind of charge _____ each other.

_____ 14. Objects with opposite charges _____ each other.

_____ 15. The ends of a magnet are called the _____.

_____ 16. The area around a magnet where the force of the magnet can act is called the _____.

_____ 17. The pushing or pulling force caused by a magnet is called _____.

_____ 18. Electricity can be produced by a _____, which uses a coil of wire and a magnet.

_____ 19. A temporary magnet formed when electric current flows through a wire coiled around certain metal cores is called an _____.

_____ 20. Particles of matter can have a positive or a _____ charge.

Label each statement as either *True* or *False*.

_____ 21. Every circuit must have an unbroken path and a <u>power source</u>.

_____ 22. A <u>parallel circuit</u> has more than one path.

_____ 23. The continuous flow of negative charges through a material is called <u>static electricity</u>.

_____ 24. Magnetism and electricity are <u>related</u>.

_____ 25. A magnet's magnetism is <u>weakest</u> at the magnet's poles.

Complete the section.

26. List two ways magnets can be used to produce electricity.

_____

_____

27. What is all matter made up of? _____

_____

28. Mr. Henry, an electrician, is looking at the plans for a new game room. All the outlets will be part of the same circuit. Would it be better to have the outlets and the lights wired in a parallel circuit or a series circuit? Explain your answer.

_____

_____

_____

_____

Chapter 6 Test

Name _____

Write the letter of the correct answer.

_____ 1. Light is a form of ____.

    A. electricity   B. energy   C. lens

_____ 2. Light travels in straight lines called ____.

    A. arrows   B. threads   C. rays

_____ 3. Objects that cannot make their own light are ____.

    A. luminous   B. opaque   C. nonluminous

_____ 4. A dark shape caused when an object blocks light is called a ____.

    A. shadow   B. cloud   C. ray

_____ 5. A transparent material used to bend light is called a ____.

    A. magnet   B. lens   C. reflection

_____ 6. A lens that bends light inward is called a ____ lens.

    A. magnifying   B. concave   C. convex

_____ 7. White light is made up of ____.

    A. all colors   B. only one color   C. some of the colors

_____ 8. Two things that use lenses are ____.

    A. eyeglasses and glass doors

    B. eyeglasses and microscopes

    C. telescopes and windows

Label each statement as either _True_ or _False_.

_____ 9. A shadow is <u>shorter</u> in the morning than it is at noon.

_____ 10. Objects that can make their own light are <u>luminous</u>.

_____ 11. The bending of light as it passes from one substance to another is called <u>refraction</u>.

_____ 12. The bouncing of light off an object is called <u>opaque</u>.

_____ 13. A <u>convex lens</u> bends light outward.

Complete each statement. One term will not be used.

> optic nerve   reflect   translucent   transparent   visible spectrum

_____14. An object that is ____ allows some light rays to pass
through it.

_____15. Objects that allow all light rays to pass through them are ____.

_____16. The colors we see are the colors that ____ from the objects
around us.

_____17. All the colors that make up light are called the ____.

Match each description with the correct part of the eye.

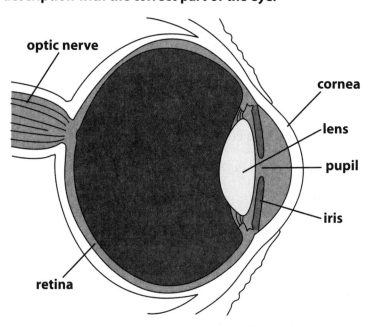

_____18. the opening in the iris that allows light to enter the
inside of the eye

_____19. the part of the eye that refracts light to focus it

_____20. the transparent, curved covering in the front of the eye

_____21. the back part of the eye where an image forms

_____22. the part of the eye that carries images to the brain

_____23. the colored part of the eye that controls how much light
enters the eye

Complete the section.

24. Circle the picture that shows the shadow in the correct position.

25. What does the Bible teach about the creation of light? _____

_____

26. The sun provides natural light. Summarize the benefits of the sun's light on Earth.

_____

_____

_____

27. Circle the order that light enters the eye.

    A. cornea → pupil → lens → retina → optic nerve

    B. optic nerve → pupil → cornea → lens → retina

    C. cornea → pupil → optic nerve → retina → lens

Chapter 7 Test

Name _____

Write the letter of the correct answer.

_____ 1. A large, flat land area on the moon's surface is called a ____.

    A. crater   B. mare   C. rille

_____ 2. A hollowed-out place on the moon's surface is called a ____.

    A. crater   B. mare   C. rille

_____ 3. A deep valley on the moon's surface is called a ____.

    A. crater   B. mare   C. rille

_____ 4. Each complete spin of the moon on its axis is called ____.

    A. a revolution   B. an ellipse   C. a rotation

_____ 5. Each complete trip of the moon around the earth is called ____.

    A. a revolution   B. an ellipse   C. a rotation

_____ 6. The shape of the moon's path around the earth is called ____.

    A. a circle   B. a sphere   C. an ellipse

_____ 7. The path the moon takes around the earth is called its ____.

    A. phase   B. orbit   C. ellipse

_____ 8. Any object that travels around another object in space is called ____.

    A. a revolution   B. a satellite   C. an ellipse

Mark the correct label for each diagram.

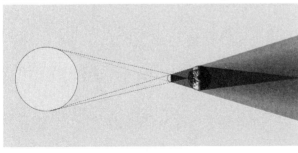

9. ○ lunar eclipse   ○ solar eclipse

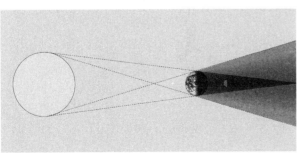

10. ○ lunar eclipse   ○ solar eclipse

Label each statement as either _True_ or _False_.

_____ 11. Psalm 33:6–9 tells us to <u>fear</u> the Lord and stand in awe of Him.

_____ 12. The moon is <u>larger</u> than the earth.

_____ 13. The moon is a <u>natural satellite</u> of the earth.

_____ 14. The gravity of the earth keeps the moon in its <u>orbit</u>.

_____ 15. You would weigh <u>more</u> on the moon than on the earth.

Write the letter of the correct phase.

A. first quarter   C. waning crescent   E. waxing crescent
B. full moon   D. waning gibbous

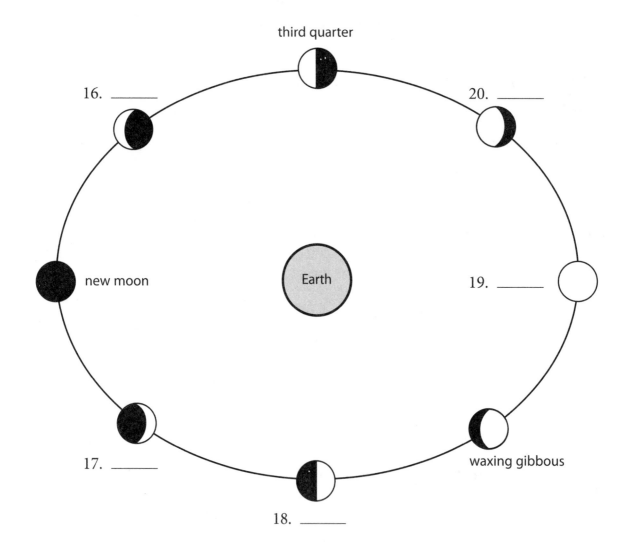

Chapter 7 Test

Science 4

Complete each statement. Some words will not be used.

mass   starlight   sunlight   waning   waxing   weight

_____ 21. When gravity changes, an object's ____ also changes.

_____ 22. A measurement of the amount of matter an object has is called its ____.

_____ 23. When the lit part of the moon is getting smaller, we say the moon is ____.

_____ 24. The moon's light comes from ____ reflecting off the moon's surface.

Complete the section.

25. What are the two choices in finding the answer to the origin of the moon?

_____

_____

26. Explain why we always see the same side of the moon.

_____

_____

27. The subject of the origin of the moon is being discussed at a campfire. Dennis believes the moon broke away from the earth and began orbiting the earth. Julie believes the earth and the moon formed from a cloud of dust and gas. Andrew believes the earth's gravity pulled the moon from outer space into its orbit. Describe what a Christian believes about the moon's origin.

_____

_____

_____

Chapter 8 Test

Name _____

Match each description with the correct term.

_____ 1. water vapor changing into water to form clouds

_____ 2. a stream of water moving like a river through the ocean

_____ 3. the cause of most waves and surface currents

_____ 4. any moisture that falls from the air and reaches the ground

_____ 5. water changing into a gas or water vapor

_____ 6. the movement of water from the earth to the air and back to earth

A. condensation
B. current
C. evaporation
D. precipitation
E. water cycle
F. wind

Label the diagram of the water cycle. Use terms from the section above.

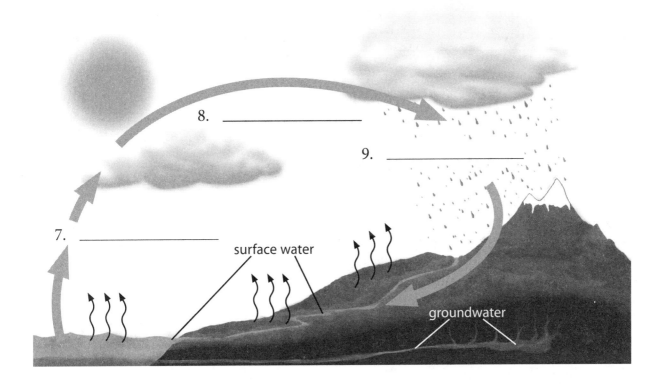

8. _____

9. _____

7. _____

surface water

groundwater

Label each statement as either *True* or *False*.

_____10. <u>Germs</u> are tiny plants and animals that live and move throughout the ocean.

_____11. A tide is caused by the way <u>gravity</u> varies depending on the distance of the earth from the sun and moon.

_____12. A <u>wave</u> is the up-and-down movement on the surface of the water.

_____13. The rise and fall of the water level of the ocean is called a <u>current</u>.

_____14. The usual weather of an area over a long period of time is called the <u>climate</u>.

Complete each statement. Some words will not be used.

| Arctic | land | Pacific | water |
| fresh | minerals | temperature | wind |

_____15. Almost three-fourths of the earth is covered by _____.

_____16. Water can be either salt water or _____ water.

_____17. Fresh water carries nutrients and _____ to the ocean.

_____18. Surface currents are caused by _____ changes.

_____19. The smallest and shallowest ocean is the _____ Ocean.

_____20. Most waves are caused by _____.

Write the letter of the correct answer.

_____21. Tides happen in different places because the earth rotates as the _____ pulls on it.

    A. moon   B. sun   C. stars

_____22. Many bodies of water have two high tides and _____ low tides each day.

    A. two   B. three   C. four

Write the letter of the correct answer.

_____23. Temperature changes and the amount of salt in the water control the ____.

    A. surface currents

    B. deep ocean currents

    C. Gulf Stream

_____24. The four main oceans are the ____ Oceans.

    A. Antarctic, Atlantic, Indian, and Pacific

    B. Arctic, Atlantic, Indian, and Southern

    C. Arctic, Atlantic, Indian, and Pacific

_____25. Both the ocean floor and the earth's surface have ____.

    A. salt in the water

    B. mountains, valleys, and plains

    C. currents and tsunamis

_____26. The Pacific Ocean is the ____ ocean.

    A. largest and shallowest

    B. smallest and deepest

    C. largest and deepest

Complete the section.

27. Describe what we know from the Bible about the origin of sea creatures.

_____

_____

_____

28. Name two ways that wind determines the size of waves.

_____

_____

Chapter 9 Test

Name _____

Write the letter of the correct answer.

_____ 1. The layer of soil that contains humus is called ____.

    A. bedrock

    B. topsoil

    C. subsoil

_____ 2. The layer in which most plants grow is called ____.

    A. bedrock

    B. topsoil

    C. subsoil

_____ 3. The layer that is made of solid, unweathered rock under layers of soil is called ____.

    A. bedrock

    B. topsoil

    C. subsoil

_____ 4. Small bits of weathered rock and other material are called ____.

    A. abrasion

    B. humus

    C. sediment

_____ 5. Sediment that is deposited at the mouth of a river makes the mouth of the river ____.

    A. deeper

    B. narrower

    C. shallower

_____ 6. The moving of bits of weathered material from one place to another is called ____.

    A. gravity

    B. erosion

    C. sediment

_____ 7. The dropping of sediment in a new place is called ____.

    A. deposition

    B. landforms

    C. abrasion

_____ 8. An area of sediment that builds up at the mouth of a river is called _____.

    A. a delta

    B. a butte

    C. an avalanche

_____ 9. Soil is made of _____.

    A. water, humus, and fossils

    B. weathered rock, air, and mesas

    C. weathered rock, water, air, and humus

_____ 10. Two types of landforms are _____.

    A. mountains and dunes

    B. gorges and rivers

    C. dunes and lakes

_____ 11. Three things that can cause rocks to weather are _____.

    A. wind, tornados, and plants

    B. wind, water, and plants

    C. water, rain, and plants

_____ 12. The three sizes of weathered rock found in soil are _____.

    A. pebbles, gravel, and clay

    B. sand, pebbles, and clay

    C. sand, silt, and clay

_____ 13. Two kinds of sudden erosion caused by gravity are _____.

    A. landslides and avalanches

    B. wind and water

    C. wind and avalanches

Match each definition with the correct term.

_____14. occurs when water or wind gradually wears away rock by friction

_____15. the process of water in and around rocks and soil freezing and expanding, breaking up the rocks

_____16. the rapid downhill movement of a large amount of soil and rocks

_____17. a huge sheet of ice that stays frozen all year

_____18. a sudden downhill movement of a large amount of snow and ice

> A. abrasion
> B. avalanche
> C. frost weathering
> D. glacier
> E. landslide

Write the correct word to complete each statement.

_____19. The process of breaking down rocks into smaller pieces is called _____.

_____20. The soil layer that is mostly coarse, weathered rocks and does not contain humus is the _____.

_____21. Volcanoes and earthquakes can push land _____.

_____22. A moraine is a hill formed by a _____.

Label each statement as either *True* or *False*.

_____23. Decayed plant and animal material in soil is called sediment.

_____24. Erosion always happens quickly.

_____25. Glaciers can pick up sediment and rocks.

_____26. U-shaped valleys where ponds and lakes form can be caused by glaciers.

Complete the section.

27. List two ways that the activities of people can cause erosion.

_____

_____

28. Explain how a volcano can form an island.

_____

_____

_____

_____

Chapter 10 Test

Name _____

Mark *R* if the statement refers to renewable resources.
Mark *N* if the statement refers to nonrenewable resources.

R   N

○   ○   1. This type of resource cannot be easily replaced.

○   ○   2. This type of resource can be replaced naturally in a short amount of time.

○   ○   3. Trees and soil are examples of this type of resource.

○   ○   4. Coal, oil, copper, and iron ore are examples of this type of resource.

○   ○   5. This type of resource includes fossil fuels.

Write the letter of the correct answer.

_____ 6. A material in nature that God made for our use is called ____.

       A. a natural resource   B. conservation   C. a solar resource

_____ 7. Most fresh water that people use comes from ____.

       A. the oceans   B. the Great Lakes   C. groundwater

_____ 8. A large area of land where garbage is buried is called a ____.

       A. trash can   B. recycling center   C. landfill

_____ 9. Electricity produced by moving water is called ____ energy.

       A. solar   B. hydroelectric   C. wind

_____ 10. Power produced by a flow of air is called ____ energy.

       A. wind   B. hydroelectric   C. solar

_____ 11. Power produced by energy from the sun is called ____ energy.

       A. hydroelectric   B. wind   C. solar

_____ 12. When plants or animals are buried quickly under great pressure, ____ form.

       A. petrified fuels   B. fossil fuels   C. ancient fuels

_____ 13. When people cut down trees for use, it is called ____.

       A. harvesting   B. logging   C. conserving

Write the correct word to complete each statement.

_____ 14. Water is one of our most important natural resources because it is a _____ of most land animals and plants.

_____ 15. One way farmers can help maintain the soil is by controlling _____.

_____ 16. Another way farmers can help maintain the soil is by _____ nutrients.

_____ 17. To lessen the effect of harvesting trees, an area may be used for a different purpose or may be _____ with new trees.

Label each statement as either _True_ or _False_.

_____ 18. We should conserve water because we recognize this resource is from <u>God</u> and we need to use it wisely.

_____ 19. Three renewable energy resources are water, wind, and <u>fossil fuels</u>.

_____ 20. Fossil fuels can cause <u>pollution</u>.

_____ 21. Sometimes trucks, trains, and ships carrying <u>solar</u> fuels leak or spill.

Write _reduce, reuse,_ or _recycle_ next to each definition.

_____ 22. use a resource over and over

_____ 23. process a new item from something old

_____ 24. decrease the use of resources

Complete the section.

25. Explain why we should be good stewards of the earth.

_____

_____

_____

26. In order to be good stewards of our resources, it is important to reduce, reuse, and recycle things that we use. Explain at least one way you can help at home using each of these methods.

Reduce: _____

_____

Reuse: _____

_____

Recycle: _____

_____

Chapter 11 Test

Name _____

Write the letter of the correct answer.

_____ 1. What are the squeezing movements made by the esophagus muscles as food moves to the stomach?

A. peristalsis

B. enzymes

C. sphincters

_____ 2. What is the liquidlike mixture of food formed when the juices in the stomach break down swallowed food?

A. saliva

B. bile

C. chyme

_____ 3. What is the name of the flap of tissue that closes to keep food out of the trachea?

A. esophagus

B. epiglottis

C. sphincter

_____ 4. How do the teeth help in digestion?

A. make food soft and wet

B. tear and crush food to help break it down

C. push food around inside the mouth

_____ 5. What is one way that the tongue helps in digestion?

A. provides stored energy and helps insulate the body

B. breaks down food for digestion

C. pushes small ball of food toward the back of the throat to be swallowed

_____ 6. What is one of the jobs that saliva has in digestion?

A. breaks down food for digestion

B. helps break down food into chyme

C. pushes food around inside the mouth

_____ 7. What is one way that the gastric juices help in digestion?

    A. help the stomach break down food

    B. react to chemicals in the food

    C. build and repair the body

_____ 8. What digestive organ produces insulin and makes enzymes that break down food into nutrients that can be absorbed?

    A. gallbladder

    B. pancreas

    C. small intestine

_____ 9. What organ stores excess bile from the liver and releases it when needed?

    A. gallbladder

    B. pancreas

    C. large intestine

_____ 10. What organ produces bile and filters poison and wastes from the blood?

    A. gallbladder

    B. liver

    C. small intestine

_____ 11. What are the five basic food groups?

    A. fruits, protein, dairy, vegetables, and grains

    B. fruits, protein, fats, vegetables, and vitamins

    C. fruits, minerals, dairy, vegetables, and carbohydrates

Label the parts of the digestive system.

esophagus
large intestine
mouth
small intestine
stomach

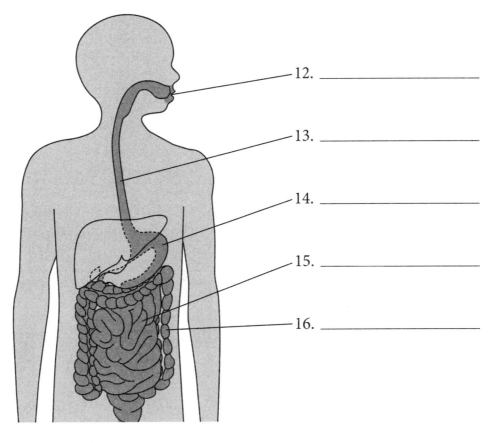

12. _____

13. _____

14. _____

15. _____

16. _____

Write the correct word to complete each statement.

_____ 17. To help you know how much of each food group you
need, the food groups are displayed in a _____.

_____ 18. Nutrients from food are absorbed into the blood as
chyme passes through the _____.

_____ 19. A sphincter is a ring of _____ that control an opening.

_____ 20. Special clusters of cells on the tongue that react to
chemicals in food are called _____.

_____ 21. The stretchy storage bag in the digestive tract below the
esophagus is called the _____.

_____ 22. The nutrients that provide stored energy and help
insulate the body are called _____.

Complete the section.

23. Explain why good nutrition is important to Christians.

_____

_____

24. Name the four basic tastes.

_____   _____

_____   _____

25. The soccer coach has suggested that you eat more protein along with having a healthy diet. Explain how eating more protein will help your body.

_____

_____

_____

_____

Chapter 12 Test

Mark *V* if the statement refers to a voluntary muscle.
Mark *I* if the statement refers to an involuntary muscle.

V   **I**

◯   ◯   1. muscles that work without your control

◯   ◯   2. muscles you can control

◯   ◯   3. most skeletal muscles

◯   ◯   4. the smooth muscles of the organs

◯   ◯   5. facial muscles

Write the letter of the correct answer.

_____ 6. What kind of joints does the skull have?

     A. immovable

     B. hinge

     C. pivot

_____ 7. When a joint is twisted too hard, what is the injury to the ligaments, tendons, and blood vessels called?

     A. strain

     B. fracture

     C. sprain

_____ 8. When a bone is put under too much pressure, what is the crack or break called?

     A. sprain

     B. fracture

     C. strain

_____ 9. What are two jobs of bones?

     A. support the body and allow side-to-side movement

     B. support the body and protect the organs

     C. control the muscles and provide the right kinds of food

_____ 10. What are two more jobs of bones?

     A. produce blood cells and store minerals

     B. produce cartilage and store vitamins

     C. mend tendons and restore damaged blood cells

_____11. How do muscles work together in pairs?

    A. Both muscles contract at the same time.

    B. One muscle moves from side-to-side while the other muscle relaxes.

    C. One muscle contracts while the other muscle relaxes.

_____12. What does the skeletal muscular system include?

    A. the bones and the muscles attached to them

    B. the bones, the muscles, and the organs

    C. the bones, the muscles, and the spinal cord

_____13. What kind of movement does a hinge joint allow?

    A. back-and-forth movement

    B. side-to-side movement

    C. movement in many directions

_____14. What kind of movement does a pivot joint allow?

    A. back-and-forth movement

    B. side-to-side movement

    C. movement in many directions

_____15. What are the two kinds of voluntary muscles?

    A. skeletal and cardiac muscles

    B. skeletal and smooth muscles

    C. skeletal and facial muscles

Label the bones in the skeleton.

femur
patella
pelvis
ribs
skull

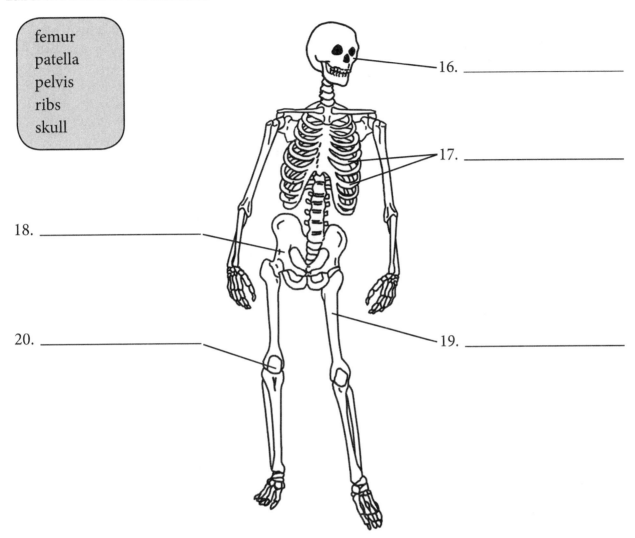

16. _____

17. _____

18. _____

20. _____

19. _____

Match each definition with the correct word.

_____21. a group of stretchy tissues that moves part of the body

_____22. a strong, elastic tissue that connects bones

_____23. strong, flexible tissue that is found between the joints and cushions them

_____24. a place where two or more bones come together

_____25. a bone in the spine that protects the spinal cord

A. cartilage
B. joint
C. ligament
D. muscle
E. vertebra

Complete the section.

26. List the three things that bones and muscles need to be healthy.

  _____

  _____

  _____

27. How can Christians use knowledge of the body system to obey God?

  _____

  _____

  _____